D0258768

LET'S VISIT THE FARM

by Ella Bruce

"There's the bus, right up to time!" cried Betty to her father. Quickly they climbed out of the landrover, crossed the road to the stop and the big green monster pulled up beside them.

"Hello Tommy!" they called out to the young boy who jumped down the steps carrying a duffle bag. Betty's cousin Tommy was too excited to reply. But as they drove back to Uncle Ned's farm in the landrover he told Betty and her father that he had quite made up his mind to be a farmer like his uncle when he grew up and he wanted to learn all about every kind of modern farming there was.

"Then," said Uncle Ned "You'll have to come here as often as you can to see what goes on at different times of the year."

"And Mummy and I can take him to the Hill Farm to see the sheep and the Dairy Farm to see where all the milk comes from," added Betty.

When they arrived in the yard Aunt Molly was there to welcome them. In the large airy kitchen a table was set for tea. Aunt Molly had spent the afternoon baking and Tommy just didn't know where to begin. There was home-made bread, scones, cakes, meat paste and jam.

After tea Tommy helped Betty feed the chickens and collect the eggs while his aunt took in some washing off the line. Aunt Molly kept chickens so that there were always lovely fresh eggs for breakfast.

It was just after Christmas and at Beech Tree Farm there was frost on the ground and snow on the hills. Uncle Ned's was an arable and beef-stock farm. So next day he took Tommy out to the fields where the men were working. Lime was being spread and this was followed by ploughing. The plough was turning up the earth and the worms and following it were crowds of seagulls and rooks. Uncle Ned said they were as artful as a waggon-load of monkeys. They knew where to get a meal without working for it.

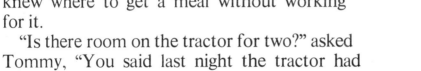

"Is there room on the tractor for two?" asked Tommy, "You said last night the tractor had taken the place of the horse and that you used to ride on the horse when you were a boy.

His uncle laughed and gave him a knowing look. "Why, you're as artful as those birds. But I'm afraid tractors are far more dangerous. You see, most of the machinery is exposed. Not like a car. Besides, there's only room for the driver. But you just watch Jim from here and see how carefully he keeps his eyes on the furrows both behind and in front and how clever he is at keeping them straight."

Tommy wanted to know what was to be sown in the field. "Oats," said his uncle, "but before that it will be harrowed and gone over with the cultivator. Then, after sowing, it will be fertilized and harrowed again."

His next visit was at Easter when Aunt Molly had a nice surprise for Tommy. They were all going to the Hill Farm for the day and were to picnic where the sheep and their lambs were now grazing. The sun was shining and it was warm and they were joined by the two children from the farm, Mary and Richard, and also Rover and Daisy, the two sheep dogs.

Tommy loved watching the lambs frisking and playing round their mothers. Betty wanted to pick one up but she was not allowed to touch them. Mother sheep would object to the scent of a human being and, like as not, have nothing more to do with her baby, but Mary said she could feed three orphan lambs when they went down to Aunt Caroline's and Uncle John's for tea. So Betty fed the lambs with bottles of milk. They were very greedy and bleated loudly until their tummies were full.

After tea Uncle John took Tommy round the farm and showed him the pens where the lambs were born. He told him the sheep were brought down from the hills in winter for shelter and fed on turnips and hay.

"Do Rover and Daisy bring them down?", asked Tommy, "I'd love to see them at work."

"And so you shall when you come again in the autumn", Uncle John assured him.

At this time there was quite a lot of activity on Beech Tree Farm. Oats and barley and sugar-beet were being sown and potatoes planted. The cattle were turned out to grass.

Uncle Ned took Tommy to the meadows and told him to look at the grass closely. "It's not any old grass," he explained. "There's timothy, rye-grass, cocksfoot and red clover amongst that lot. All good nourishing food for the animals."

"What do they eat during the winter?" asked Tommy. His uncle turned and pointed to a tall cylinder like a huge fat chimney that seemed to dominate the whole farm. "That's the silo. We cut some of the grass in June, add minerals and feed it all into the silo and when winter comes it's fed to the cattle along with turnips and hay."

Next morning Aunt Molly drove the two children to Mr Martin's dairy farm. "Because," insisted Betty "Tommy *must* see the baby calves."

"And the milking?" asked her cousin.

"Not today I'm afraid, Tommy." Aunt Molly started up the engine of the car. "It's in between milking times but we'll make a point of going again when I'm not so busy."

Tommy thought the calves were like big shaggy dogs. Betty, who seemed to know everything, told him they were taken away from their mothers soon after birth and fed by hand with milk until they could lap from a bucket. She asked the dairyman if she could feed one to show Tommy how it was done.

Tommy had read a lot about haymaking in the old days when everybody helped gather the hay and toss it up onto the cart. So he was very keen to see what modern methods were like.

His holiday in June took him right into the haymaking season and he raced Betty out into the fields immediately after one of Aunt Betty's scrumptious meals. There were two tractors working because Jim and his pal Charlie wanted to get the crop baled before the rain came that was forecast during the night

Charlie was turning the hay and "fluffing it up" so that it would dry better and Jim was following the rows which Charlie had turned that morning with the baler. Tommy watched how the baler gathered a bunch of hay, worked it into an oblong bundle, tied it securely and *then* deposited five or six of the bundles on the ground. And all this was manoeuvred by Jim from the tractor.

"Whew! Jim must be awfully clever to judge just when to pull the levers and things," cried Tommy, "I wish we could help like they did in the old days. It must have been fun then."

"Well, we could go round and see that the bundles are neatly stacked," Betty suggested, "Oh look! there's a mouse. It's been disturbed having its supper. I hope it isn't hurt."

Uncle Ned next day was climbing into the landrover when he spotted Tommy in the distance playing with Jack, the farm dog.

"Hey!" he shouted, "Want to go sheep shearing? Get hold of Betty. But be quick, I'm in a hurry."

The two children were not long in arriving, breathless with anticipation. "I've some business up at Hill Farm," said Uncle Ned, "and they're shearing today. You might as well see all you can even if you're not going to be a sheep farmer." He grinned and gave Betty a wink.

Tommy laughed and screwed up his nose. "Who said I'm not? I haven't made up my mind yet. Every type of farming is so jolly interesting."

When they were near the farm Betty suddenly asked her father to stop. "There are Aunt Caroline's pigs. And I believe there are some babies. If you drop us off here, Daddy, you can go on and we can follow on foot."

The pigs were in a field which had been turned up by their snouts in search of appetizing roots. There were four white pigs and their families. One mother pig was friendly and liked to be scratched behind the ear. The piglets squealed so loudly that Betty and Tommy could not hear each other speak.

"Let's go on to the sheep shearing," yelled Betty putting her hands over her ears, "although I think it will be just as noisy."

The loud baa-ing of sheep guided Betty and Tommy to the shearing yard. There they saw three men busy at their job of taking off the heavy woollen coats of the animals with electric shears. The shorn sheep looked very sorry for themselves but Uncle John said they soon got used to their short coats, in fact they were much happier now the warm weather had set in. They were hustled out into a field when the operation was over. The dogs, meanwhile, were guiding the others through another gate into the yard.

Betty and Tommy went over to Bill, the shepherd, who was in a corner by himself. First he sheared round the neck, then down the front, then turning the sheep this way and that had the whole fleece off in one piece in no time at all. He told them that years ago only hand shears were used, which not only needed more effort but was a much longer process.

"Where does the fleece go when it leaves the farm?" asked Tommy. Bill said the wool from the Blackface or hill breed, which his uncle had here, was used for carpets, tweed and knitwear according to the coarseness or fineness of the hair.

The Summer Holidays came at last and every one was busy on the farm. Grass was being mown for the winter silage. Tommy watched it being fed into the great tall silo. The seed potato crop was ready for rogueing. Tommy laughed and said what a funny word to use.

"Not at all," explained his uncle, "It means just what it says, and it's a very skilled job. We mostly have students who take a course in rogueing before they come here. It means picking out the undesirable potatoes from a crop while still in the ground, like those of another variety that have got in by mistake, or those that are diseased—in fact rogues."

The students came every day by bus until the job was finished. Tommy enjoyed talking to them in their lunch break and decided to go to an Agricultural College immediately he left school. After that he saw the potatoes sprayed against blight. On some of the larger farms, his uncle said, it was done by helicopter.

His promised visit to the dairy farm to see the milking was this time taken alone with Uncle Ned as Betty was going to a party.

When they got there the cows were being brought in from the fields down a long lane to the collecting yard. Tommy was thrilled to be asked to help. From the yard the cows waited their turn to go into the milking parlour, where they got a ration of food and were soon milked. The milk went along a pipe to a stainless steel refrigerated tank. It was collected daily by a big motor tanker.

The most exciting time at Beech Tree Farm was when the corn crops were being harvested. They were the results of most of the work put into the land throughout the year.

While Tommy was there in August the barley and oats were cut. He just couldn't keep away from the big combine harvester. The weather was so hot that every time the children went into the fields Aunt Molly gave them bottles of lemonade to drink and home-made buns in a bag.

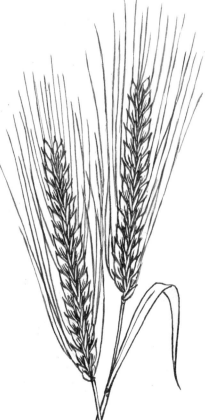

Jim was on one machine and Charlie on the other. The harvesters went up and down the field like two monsters out of a science fiction film, thought Tommy. Sometimes rabbits or hares ran out of the corn in front of them.

Uncle Ned came and pointed out the various parts of the harvester and Tommy saw how the front part cut the stalks close to the ground, how, after being drawn into the machine by a revolving wheel the oats were threshed and the grain separated from the straw which was pushed out of the back and the grain retained in a container. Then a truck drove alongside and the grain was emptied through a long tube into the truck which, when full, drove back to the farm to be replaced by an empty one. The grain was then cleaned and stored for sale.

The end of the Summer Holiday came all too soon. Tommy was sorry he was going to miss the potatoes being gathered as it was no longer done by hand. A big machine plucked them from the earth, transferred them to a conveyer belt where two or three people stood throwing out the stones and sods of earth. The potatoes were then loaded into a truck, like the grain, through a tube and taken to the storage barn. And it all happened while the harvester moved along at a snail's pace up and down the field.

The turnips were stored for winter feed for the cattle and when Tommy came in the autumn the wheat had been sown for next year's crop.

"Now," cried Betty, "Tommy will be able to see the sheep brought down from the hills. If you're too busy to take us, Mummy, we could walk to Uncle John's across the fields."

Aunt Molly was making jam so the children set out after an early breakfast and were in time to watch Rover and Daisy working a flock of sheep. The shepherd walked behind and every now and again gave a low whistle. The dogs responded immediately, rounded up the strays and guided the flock neatly into the farm pens.

After a most exciting day at Hill Farm, Aunt Molly called for them in the car.

Tommy sleepily said he thought he would like to be a sheep farmer but, of course, there was plenty of time for him to change his mind.

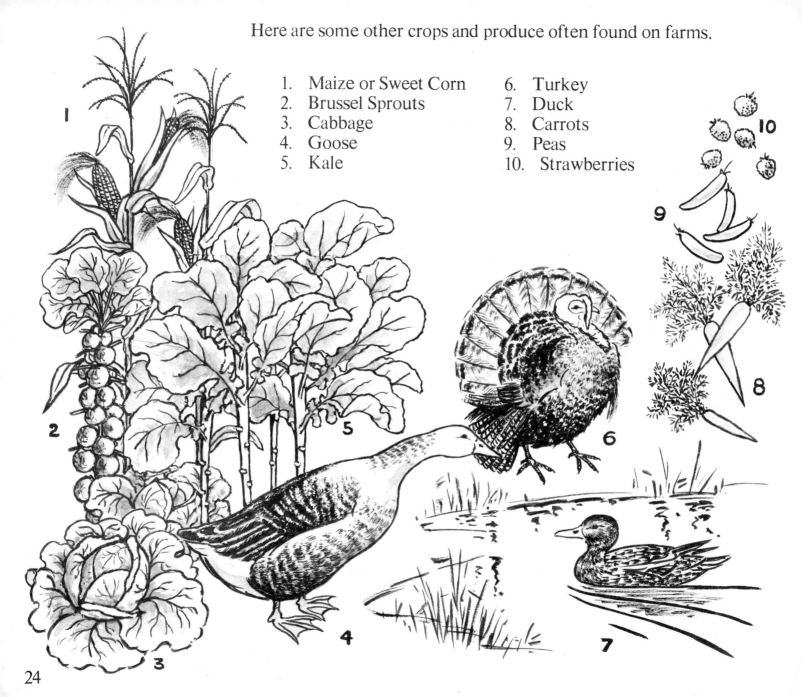

Here are some other crops and produce often found on farms.

1. Maize or Sweet Corn
2. Brussel Sprouts
3. Cabbage
4. Goose
5. Kale
6. Turkey
7. Duck
8. Carrots
9. Peas
10. Strawberries